w-priced Bantam Book
mpletely reset in a type face
easy reading, and was printed
ates. It contains the complete
original hard-cover edition.
WORD HAS BEEN OMITTED.

RL 6, IL 8+

"NEVADA"
/ published by arrangement with
& Row, Publishers, Inc.

INTING HISTORY
AMERICAN MAGAZINE 1926—1927
tion published January 1928
inting ...... October 1929
nting .... November 1929
edition Published September 1929
edition published 1931
ck Reader's Service Company) edition
ublished June 1951
ngs through January 1957
edition / January 1946
ings through January 1979

SBN 0-553-12383-1

usly in the United States and Canada

blished by Bantam Books, Inc. Its trade-
e words "Bantam Books" and the por-
Registered in U.S. Patent and Trademark
countries. Marca Registrada. Bantam
Avenue, New York, New York 10019.

IE UNITED STATES OF AMERICA

SHOWDOWN

The noise that had halted Nevada came from the saloon. He strode to the nearest group of men. "What's happened?" he queried.

"We was playin' our caird games," spoke up the gambler, Ace Black, "when we heerd an awful row in the hall there. We all jumped up an' some one rushed out to see what it was. An' by Gawd—"

"Wal?" broke in Nevada, cool and grim, as Black choked.

"Lize Teller! She was layin' half naked, streamin' blood. Link Cawthorne had beat her over the head with his gun. She'll die!"

In three long bounds Nevada had reached and split the beaded door-curtain. His swift eye swept all.

"Cawthorne!" he yelled, in piercing voice that brought an instant breathless silence.

This
has been
designed f
from new
text of t
NOT O

A Bantam Bo
Harp

Serialized i
Harper e
2nd
3rd
Grosset & Dun
Coll
Walter J. Black (B

9 pri
Bant
19 pri

Published simulta

Bantam Books are
mark, consisting of
trayal of a bantam,
Office and in oth
Books, Inc., 666 F

PRINTED IN